Play Piano with...
Corinne Bailey Rae
Rihanna
Norah Jones &
Other Great Artists

Play Piano with...
Corinne Bailey Rae
Rihanna
Norah Jones &
Other Great Artists

Wise Publications
part of The Music Sales Group

London / New York / Paris / Sydney / Copenhagen / Berlin / Madrid / Tokyo

Published by
Wise Publications
14-15 Berners Street, London W1T 3LJ, UK.

Exclusive Distributors:
Music Sales Limited
Distribution Centre, Newmarket Road, Bury St Edmunds, Suffolk IP33 3YB, UK.
Music Sales Pty Limited
120 Rothschild Avenue, Rosebery, NSW 2018, Australia.

Order No. AM985358
ISBN 1-84609-505-0
This book © Copyright 2006 Wise Publications
a division of Music Sales Limited.

Music arranged, recorded and mixed by Danny Gluckstein.
Edited by Tom Farncombe.
CD mastered by Jonas Persson and John Rose.
Cover photographs:
Corinne Bailey Rae courtesy of Perou / Camera Press London,
Norah Jones courtesy of Joanne Savio / Retna and
Rihanna courtesy of Nela Konig / Retna.
Printed in the EU.

Your Guarantee of Quality
As publishers, we strive to produce every book to the highest commercial standards.
The music has been freshly engraved and the book has been carefully designed to
minimise awkward page turns and to make playing from it a real pleasure.
Particular care has been given to specifying acid-free, neutral-sized paper made from
pulps which have not been elemental chlorine bleached.
This pulp is from farmed sustainable forests and was produced with special regard for the environment.
Throughout, the printing and binding have been planned to ensure a sturdy,
attractive publication which should give years of enjoyment.
If your copy fails to meet our high standards, please inform us and we will gladly replace it.

www.musicsales.com

Almost Blue

Words & Music by Elvis Costello

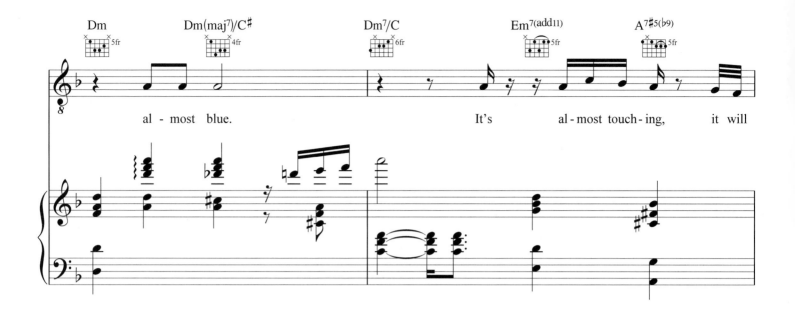

al - most blue. It's al - most touch - ing, it will

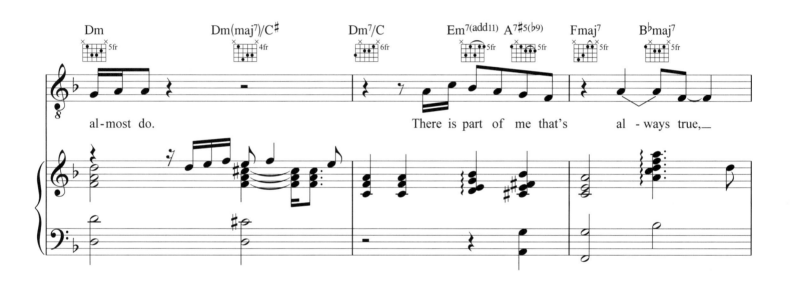

al - most do. There is part of me that's al - ways true,___

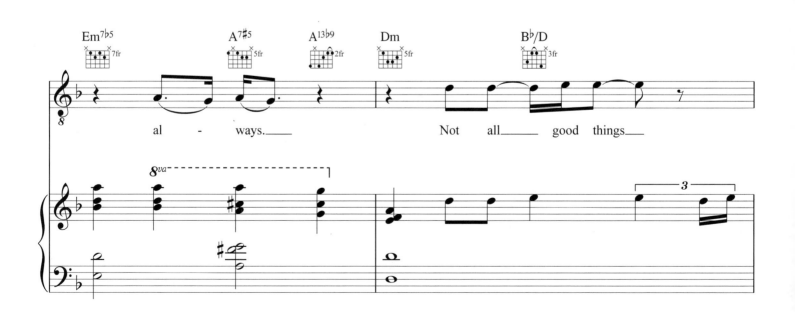

al - ways.___ Not all___ good things___

Blue Shoes

Words & Music by Mike Batt

4. These blue shoes_____ seem to suit me well,_____ when I feel like hell,_____ as
I do now that you're gone._____ Lost and lone-ly since you stopped car-ing.
I've been wear-ing my new shoes._____ I've been wear-ing my blue shoes._____

Choux Pastry Heart

Words & Music by Corinne Bailey Rae & Teitur Lassen

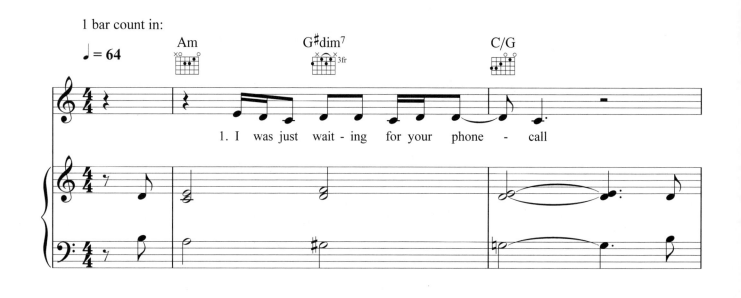

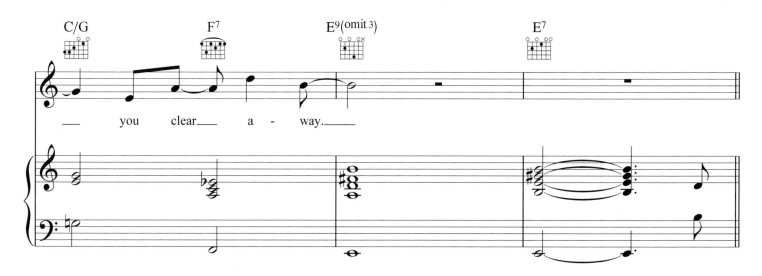

16

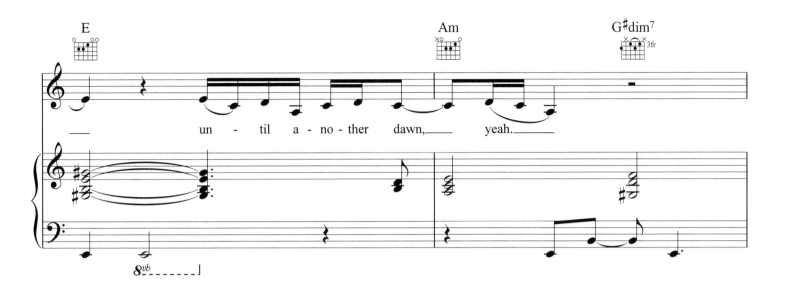

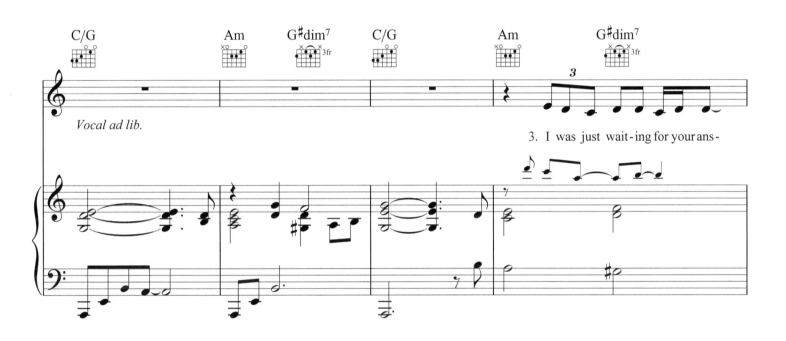

Vocal ad lib.

3. I was just wait-ing for your ans-

-wer.___ Still, you made your own a - po - lo - gies.___ I cried

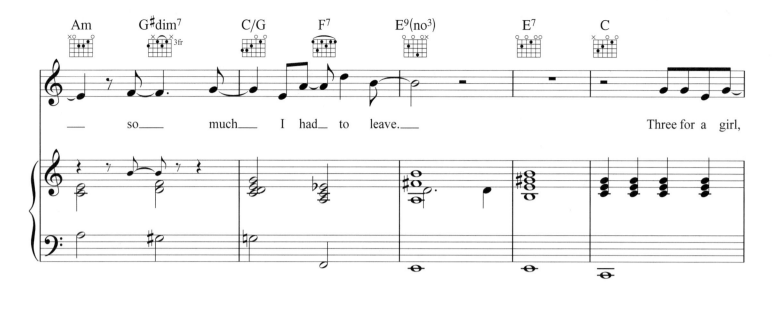

so____ much____ I had___ to leave.____   Three for a girl,

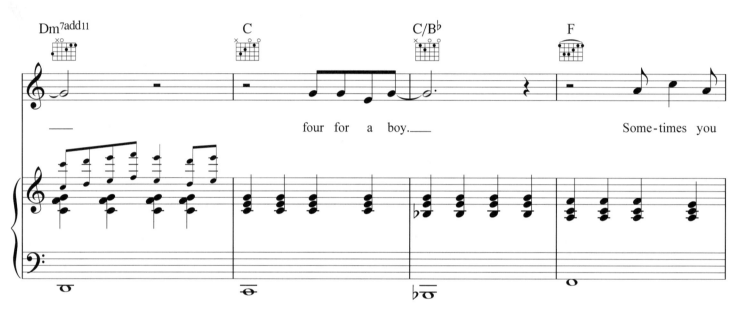

____   four for a boy.____   Some-times you

win,   ooh,_____ some times you lose._____   Don't wan-na lose____ you._

21

Dance Me To The End Of Love

Words & Music by Leonard Cohen

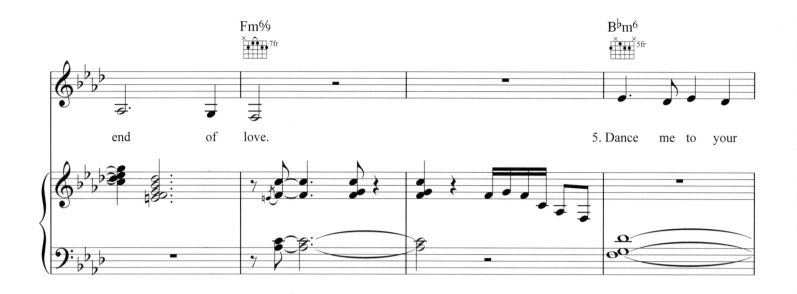

end of love.   5. Dance me to your

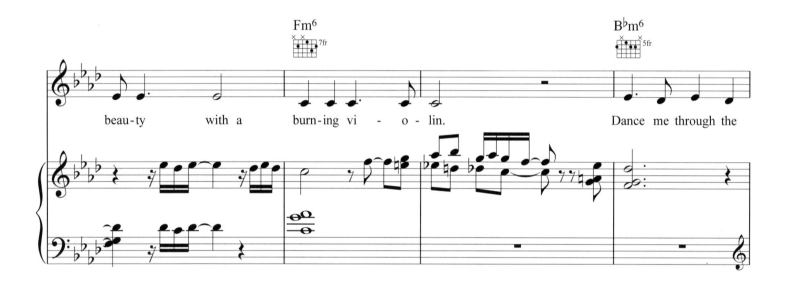

beau-ty   with a   burn-ing vi - o - lin.   Dance me through the

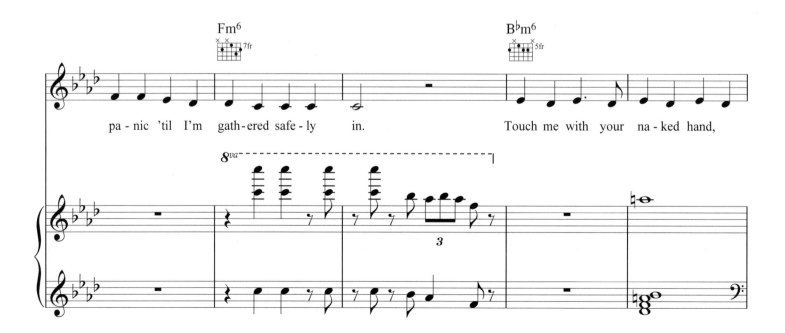

pa - nic 'til I'm gath-ered safe - ly   in.   Touch me with your na - ked hand,

The Nearness Of You

Words by Ned Washington
Music by Hoagy Carmichael

Idaho

Words & Music by Nerina Pallot

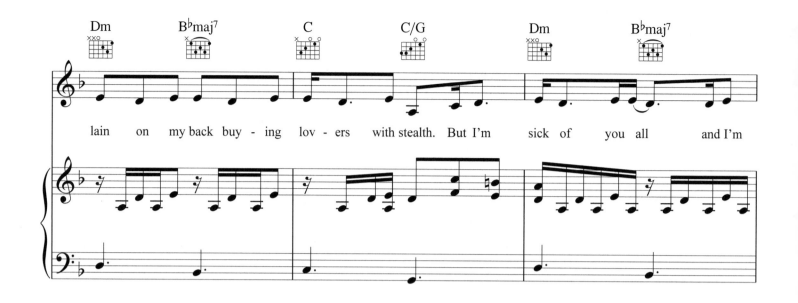

lain on my back buy-ing lov-ers with stealth. But I'm sick of you all and I'm

sick of o-pin-ions. I'm sick of this war___ I___ wage on my-self and I

don't know why I'm so gripped to go___ there.___ A u-ni-verse rid-dle that

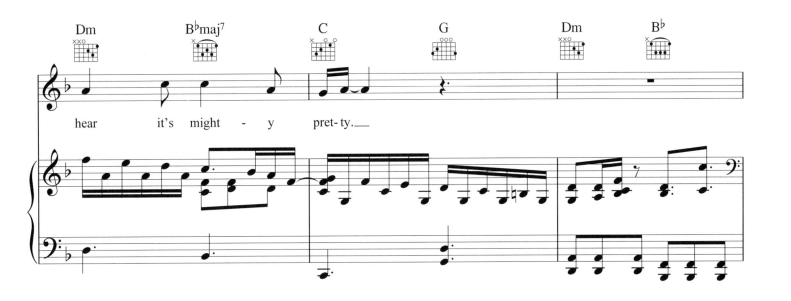

hear   it's   might - y   pret- ty.___

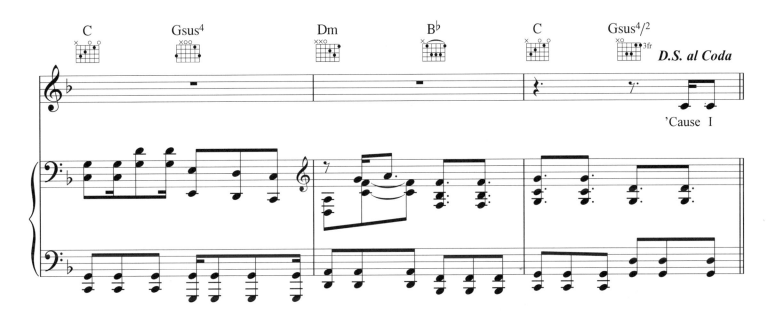

D.S. al Coda

'Cause I

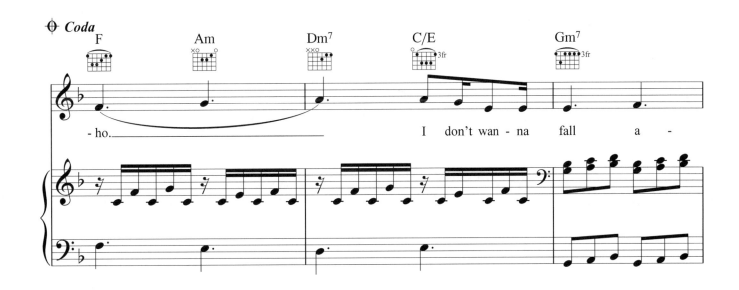

-ho.___

I   don't wan - na   fall   a -

Through The Dark

Words & Music by KT Tunstall & Martin Terefe

I walk a-way___ I look ov-er___ my shoul-der to

Unfaithful

Words & Music by
Mikkel Eriksen, Tor Erik Hermansen & Shaffer Smith

1. Sto - ry of my life, search-ing for the right. But it keeps a-void - ing me._

(2.) feel it in the air as I'm do-ing my hair, pre - par-ing for a - no - ther day._

(2° 8ve higher for first 8 bars)

be the rea - son why.___ Ev-'ry-time I walk out the door I see him die a

lit - tle more___ in - side.___ I don't wan-na hurt him an - y-more

I don't wan-na take a - way___ his life.___ I don't wan - na be___

To Coda

a mur-der- er.___

2. I a mur-der-er. Our love, his trust. I might as well take a gun and put it to his head, get it ov-er with. I don't wan-na do this an-y-more. Oh.

23456789

05/07 (62153)

CD Track Listing

Full performance demonstration tracks...

1. Almost Blue

(Costello) BMG Music Publishing Limited.

2. Blue Shoes

(Batt) Sony / ATV Music Publishing (UK) Limited.

3. Choux Pastry Heart

(Bailey Rae / Lassen) EMI Music Publishing (WP) Limited / Global Talent Publishing.

4. Dance Me To The End Of Love

(Cohen) Sony / ATV Music Publishing (UK) Limited.

5. The Nearness Of You

(Washington / Carmichael) Famous Music Publishing Limited.

6. Idaho

(Pallot) Chrysalis Music Limited.

7. Through The Dark

(Tunstall / Terefe) Sony / ATV Music Publishing (UK) Limited.

8. Unfaithful

(Eriksen / Hermansen / Smith) Zomba Music Publishers Limited / Sony /
ATV Music Publishing (UK) Limited / EMI Music Publishing Limited.

Backing tracks only (without piano)...

9. Almost Blue
10. Blue Shoes
11. Choux Pastry Heart
12. Dance Me To The End Of Love
13. The Nearness Of You
14. Idaho
15. Through The Dark
16. Unfaithful

To remove your CD from the plastic sleeve,

lift the small lip to break the perforations.

Replace the disc after use for convenient storage.